COLOR-
CODED

Color-Coded: A Therapeutic Sketch Journal Towards Personal Breakthrough For Black Folks

FIRST EDITION

DEDICATION PAGE - FOR THE CULTURE

Color-Coded is dedicated to our ancestors who have told the stories of their journeys in hopes of preparing a brighter tomorrow for future generations.

WANT TO DIG DEEPER? WE GOT YOU!

Culturally, mental health advocacy and vulnerability is a growth opportunity for people of color so we designed Color-Coded to serve as a safe place to chronicle your day however you see fit. Color-Coded is a prompting, doodling, and scribbling journal where you write down any thoughts, feelings, and emotions today, tomorrow, now, or later.

Color-Coded was designed to tackle unique, relevant, and identifiable Black experiences. Simply use the journal as a guide to releasing your emotions and inner feelings to de-clutter your brain.

In essence, Color-Coded is whatever you want it to be. A blank slate to let your mind roam free.

BUT FOR REAL...

Celebrate your wins, lean into your vulnerabilities and let your creative juices flow.

After you release what you have been holding in that day, week, month, year, or lifetime; reflect on how you feel. Hopefully, you feel a bit lighter, a bit better, and able to move forward.

Have days that you don't want to journal alone? Make it a family affair, a conversation starter, or a come to Jesus moment with others.

Each one, teach one!

LET'S GO!

1. Set a time for yourself to be uninterrupted.

2. Dare to go against the grain? Pick a random page. Not quite your style, go in order.

3. Use the illustrations and prompts as a starting point to let go.

4. Write down whatever comes to your mind. **Be real with yourself!**

5. Release and reflect.

6. Do you and express yourself freely!

DATE: _____
TIME: _____

SOMETHING NEW TO TACKLE!

HOW I FEEL TODAY:

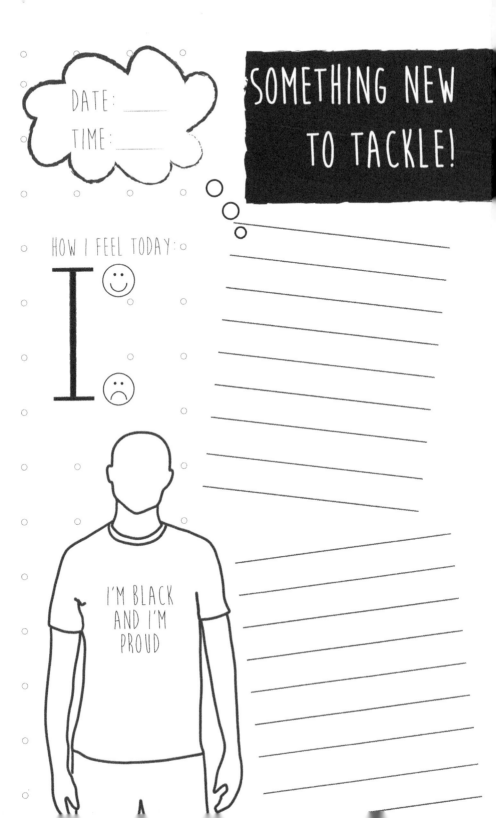

I'M BLACK AND I'M PROUD

IT'S A CELEBRATION!

DATE: _____
TIME: _____

HOW I FEEL TODAY:

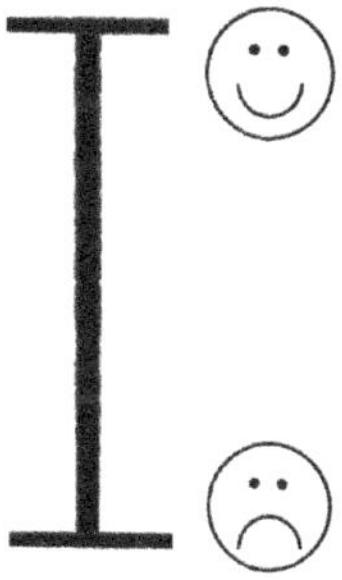

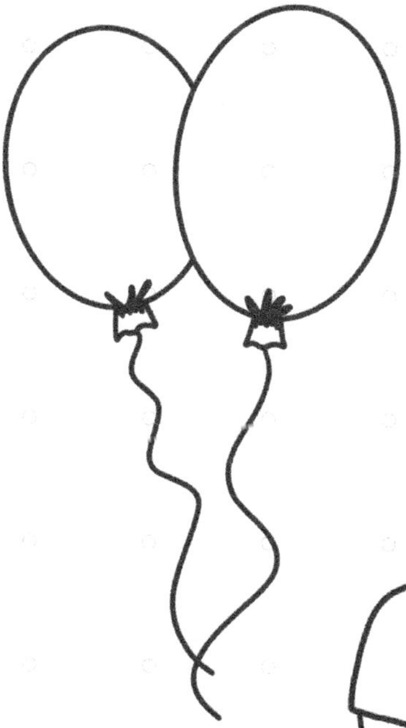

I
☺

☹

BLACK
AND
EDUCATED

RELAX

DATE: _____
TIME: _____

HOW I FEEL TODAY:

BEAUTY & BRAINS

DATE: _____

TIME: _____

IS YOUR LIFE A TRAFFIC JAM?

HOW I FEEL TODAY:

THE FLOW
OF MY DAY TODAY:

TAKE DEEP BREATHS

DATE: _____
TIME: _____

HOW I FEEL TODAY:

RESOURCEFUL WOMAN

SOLID FOUNDATION

DATE: _____
TIME: _____

HOW I FEEL TODAY:
I 😊
I 😞

STRONG
BLACK
WOMAN

_____
_____
_____

DATE: _____
TIME: _____

MY POISON

HOW I FEEL TODAY:

I 🙂

I 🙁

MELANATED
&
MINDFUL

FEAR

DATE: ______

TIME: ______

HOW I FEEL TODAY:

THAT SOMETHING IS

HOLDING ME BACK

BUILDING MY *Legacy*

DATE: _____

TIME: _____

HOW I FEEL TODAY:

I 🙂

😞

BLACK QUEEN

A RELAXING THOUGHT...

DATE: _____

TIME: _____

HOW I FEEL TODAY:

I 🙂
😞

ME, MYSELF, AND MY COMMUNITY

DATE: _____
TIME: _____

MY SPOTLIGHT MOMENT TODAY

HOW I FEEL TODAY:

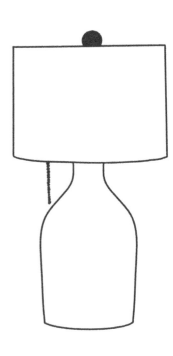

BEING TRUE
-OR-
WEARING A MASK?

DATE: _____
TIME: _____

HOW I FEEL TODAY:

I ☺

I ☹

FOINE

I'M NOT

PLAYING GAMES WITH YOU!

DATE: _____
TIME: _____

HOW I FEEL TODAY:

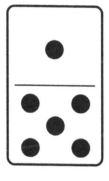
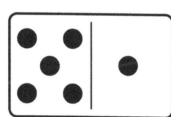

_____
_____
_____
_____
_____
_____

SAY HIS NAME

DATE: _____
TIME: _____

MY FOOD DIET

HOW I FEEL TODAY:

COURAGEOUS

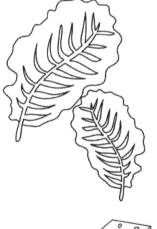

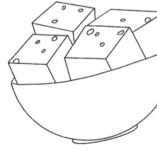

DATE: _____
TIME: _____

WHAT'S FOR DINNER?

HOW I FEEL TODAY:

IMPORTANT
TASKS TO COMPLETE TODAY:

DATE: _____
TIME: _____

Sun	Mon	Tues	Wed	Thur	Fri	Sat
		1	2	3	4	5
6	7	8	9	10	11	12
13	14	15	16	17	18	19
20	21	22	23	24	25	26
27	28	29	30			

HOW I FEEL TODAY:

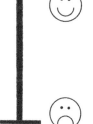

UNAPOLOGETICALLY
BLACK

DATE: _____
TIME: _____

HOW I
TURN UP

HOW I FEEL TODAY:

I ☺
☹

SORRY,
NOT SORRY

MY FEELINGS...

DATE: _____
TIME: _____

HOW I FEEL TODAY:

I'M ORIGINAL!

_____

_____

_____

_____

_____

_____

COMMITTED TO...

DATE: _____

TIME: _____

HOW I FEEL TODAY:

MADE YA LOOK.

DATE: _____
TIME: _____

HOW I FEEL TODAY:

I AM ENOUGH!

WHAT MAKES ME REGAL?

DATE: _____
TIME: _____

HOW I FEEL TODAY:

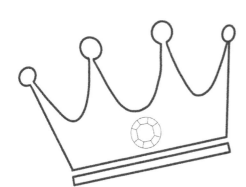

I AM WORTHY OF GOOD THINGS.

I MATTER

DATE: _____
TIME: _____

HOW I FEEL TODAY:

I CHOOSE ME.

DATE: _____

TIME: _____

THROWING

SHADE

HOW I FEEL TODAY:

I 🙂

😞

I'M SPEAKING!

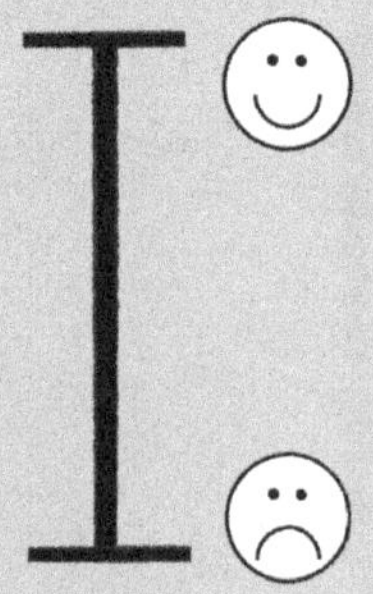

HEADED TO...

DATE: _____

TIME: _____

HOW I FEEL TODAY:

I ☺

☹

DATE: _____
TIME: _____

BRAIN

DRAIN

HOW I FEEL TODAY:

I 🙂

I ☹

I EMBRACE
SUCCESS.

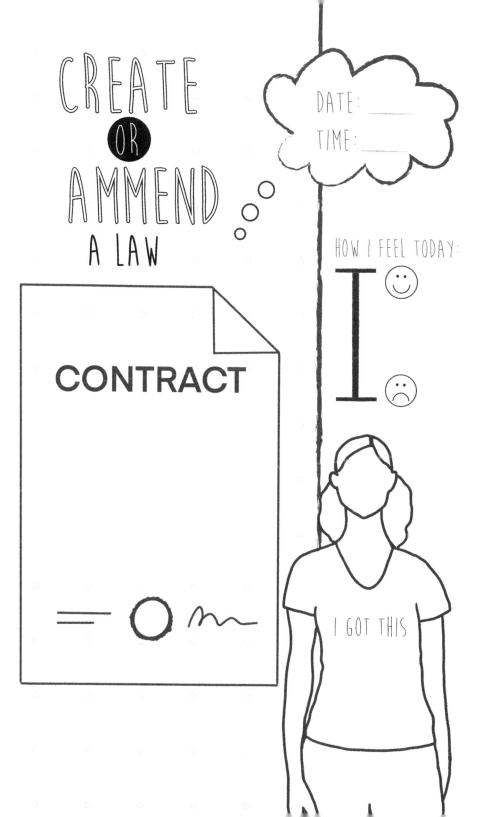

IMPORTANT
PEOPLE IN MY LIFE

DATE: _____

TIME: _____

HOW I FEEL TODAY:

_____

_____

_____

_____

_____

I WILL
ALLOW
MYSELF
GRACE.

DATE: _____
TIME: _____

PROTECTING MY
PEACE

HOW I FEEL TODAY:

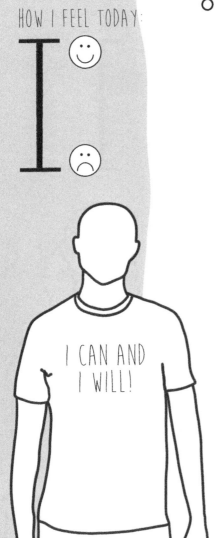

I CAN AND
I WILL!

SAVING FOR...

DATE: _____
TIME: _____

HOW I FEEL TODAY:

MY PERSONAL DEVELOPMENT

DATE: _____
TIME: _____

HOW I FEEL TODAY:

LOADING...

DATE: _____
TIME: _____

WHAT FILLS ME UP

HOW I FEEL TODAY:

E

F

I TRAIN
MY BODY

THANK -FUL FOR

DATE: _____
TIME: _____

HOW I FEEL TODAY:

I ☺

I ☹

IT'S GON' BE ALRIGHT

DATE: _____
TIME: _____

BUCKET LIST

HOW I FEEL TODAY:

LIVING MY PURPOSED LIFE

HOW I WANT TO BE REMEMBERED

DATE: _____

TIME: _____

HOW I FEEL TODAY:

RIP

BLESSED AND HIGHLY FAVORED

STAY IN YOUR LANE...
AND I'LL STAY IN MINE

DATE: _____
TIME: _____

HOW I FEEL TODAY: ☺ ☹

WALKING BY
FAITH

DATE: _____

TIME: _____

TREATED MYSELF TO...

HOW I FEEL TODAY:

PRIORITIZING MYSELF

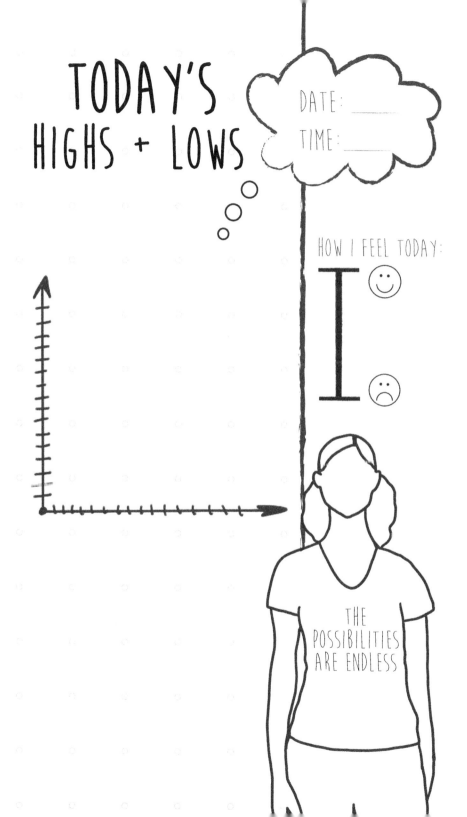

DATE: _____
TIME: _____

DIRECTING MY LIFE

HOW I FEEL TODAY:

MY BODY IS MY TEMPLE

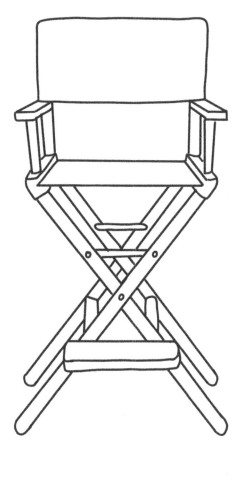

A WIN
I HAD TODAY

DATE: _____
TIME: _____

HOW I FEEL TODAY:

I WILL
NOT DWELL
IN THE
PAST.

DATE: _____

TIME: _____

MY DREAM VACATION...

HOW I FEEL TODAY:

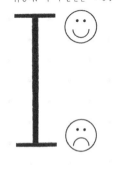

MY ANCESTOR'S DREAM

KNOCK OUT MY FEARS

DATE: _____
TIME: _____

HOW I FEEL TODAY:

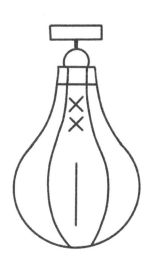

DO I HAVE TO BE #1 ALL THE TIME?

DATE: _____
TIME: _____

HOW I FEEL TODAY:

DATE: _____
TIME: _____

MY GOOD LUCK CHARM

HOW I FEEL TODAY:

I 🙂
🙁

RESILIENCY LIVES HERE!

HOLD YOUR HORSES

DATE: _____
TIME: _____

HOW I FEEL TODAY:

PUSHING THROUGH MY SELF DOUBT

DATE: _____
TIME: _____

POLITCAL
OR NAH?

HOW I FEEL TODAY:

WHAT'S YOUR EMERGENCY?

DATE: _____

TIME: _____

HOW I FEEL TODAY:

911

RELENTLESS FIGHTER

IF I HAD
WINGS
WHERE WOULD I GO?

DATE: _____

TIME: _____

HOW I FEEL TODAY: ☺ ☹

SPREAD LOVE

WHAT AM I SIPPIN' ON?

DATE: _____
TIME: _____

HOW I FEEL TODAY:

HARD WORK MAKES THE DREAM WORK

DATE: _____
TIME: _____

STOP AND SMELL THE ROSES.

HOW I FEEL TODAY:

I'M NOT THE ONE!

WHAT HAPPENED TODAY?

THE ROAD AHEAD.

DATE: _____
TIME: _____

HOW I FEEL TODAY:

DATE: _____
TIME: _____

MONEY DOESN'T GROW ON TREES!

HOW I FEEL TODAY: ☺ ☹

AN EXPENSE I CAN REDUCE:

DOIN' ME ALL DAY

WHAT'S SO FUNNY?

DATE: _____
TIME: _____

HOW I FEEL TODAY:

I 😊

😞

WHATCHU THOUGHT?

DATE: _____
TIME: _____

SOMETHING NEW
I LEARNED TODAY

HOW I FEEL TODAY:

CONFIDENT

DATE: _____
TIME: _____

WHAT AM I UPSET ABOUT?

HOW I FEEL TODAY:

NOPE, NOT TODAY

VIBING

TO...

DATE: _____

TIME: _____

HOW I FEEL TODAY:

I'M COOL

MY HELP

DATE: _____
TIME: _____

HOW I FEEL TODAY:

HOPE

MY METAMORPHOSIS

DATE: _____
TIME: _____

HOW I FEEL TODAY:

DATE: _____
TIME: _____

SAY IT LOUD

HOW I FEEL TODAY:

TRIUMPHANT

TODAY'S WORKOUT

DATE: _____

TIME: _____

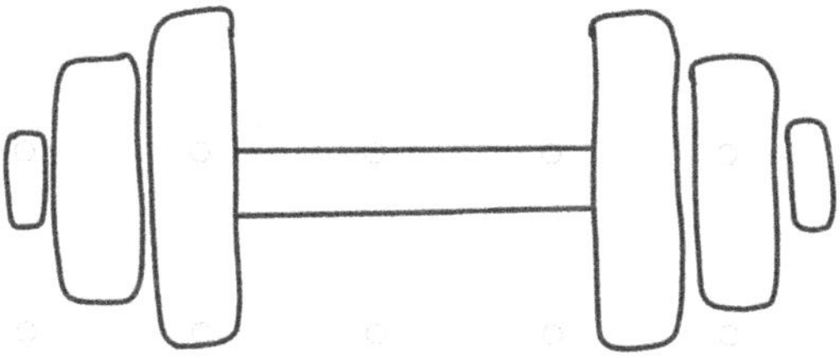

HOW I FEEL TODAY:

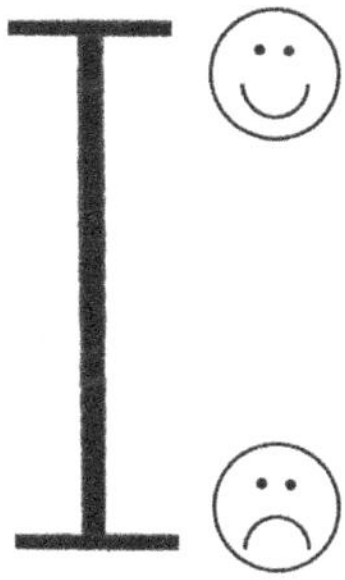

☺

☹

SUPERPOWER

MY LIKES & DISLIKES

DATE: _____
TIME: _____

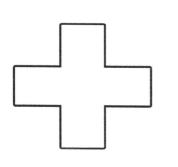

HOW I FEEL TODAY:

LOVE

DATE: _____
TIME: _____

HOW I FEEL TODAY:

SHOOT YO SHOT

MY DREAM JOB:

ONWARD AND UPWARD

WHO GOT NEXT?

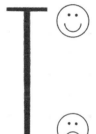

DATE: _____
TIME: _____

WORDS FOR THE NEXT GENERATION:

HOW I FEEL TODAY:

I ☺
  ☹

STAND STEADFAST

DATE: _____
TIME: _____

HOW OFTEN DO I SPEAK UP FOR MYSELF?

HOW I FEEL TODAY:

SO FORREAL!

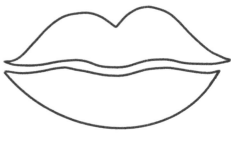

FEELING GOOD,
FEELING
GREAT!

DATE: _____
TIME: _____

HOW I FEEL TODAY:

LAUGHTER

DATE: _____
TIME: _____

MY RESPONSIBILITIES

HOW I FEEL TODAY:

BILL
$ $ $

CALL A SPADE A SPADE

HARD TRUTHS ABOUT MYSELF:

DATE: _____

TIME: _____

HOW I FEEL TODAY:

BLACK IS MY HAPPY COLOR

AM I A GOOD BEST FRIEND?

DATE: _____
TIME: _____

HOW I FEEL TODAY:

HERSTORY

DATE: _____
TIME: _____

FINDING MY

WAY OUT

HOW I FEEL TODAY:

I 😊

I 🙁

JUST
IMAGINE...

THINK OUTSIDE THE BOX

DATE: _____
TIME: _____

HOW I FEEL TODAY:

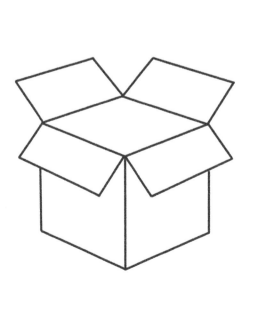

DATE: _____
TIME: _____

WHAT BROUGHT A SMILE TO MY FACE TODAY?

HOW I FEEL TODAY:

SERVE AND PROTECT?

DATE: _____
TIME: _____

HOW I FEEL TODAY:

IMPACTFUL
AND
INTENTIONAL

DATE: _____
TIME: _____

AMERICA
THE "FREE-ISH"

HOW I FEEL TODAY:

FREEDOM

WRITING A THANK YOU LETTER TO...

DATE: _____
TIME: _____

HOW I FEEL TODAY:

☺
☹

I TAKE CHANCES

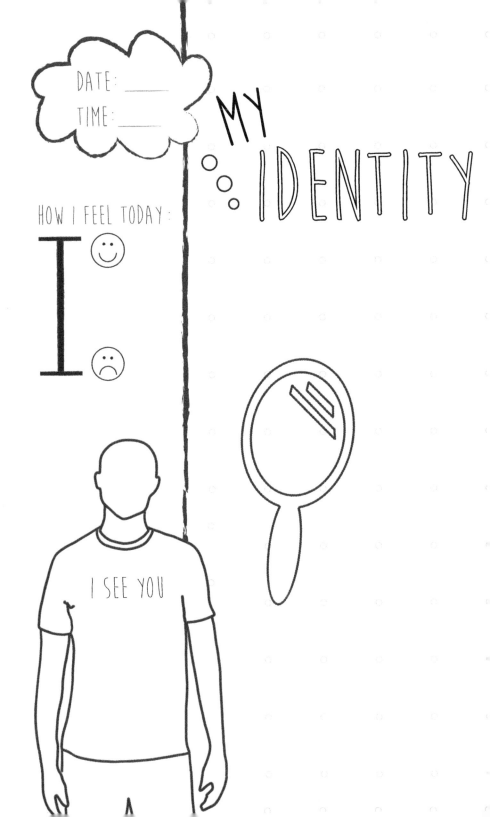

DO I KNOW MY RIGHTS?

DATE: _____

TIME: _____

HOW I FEEL TODAY:

HEALING PAST TRAUMAS

DATE: _____

TIME: _____

HOW I FEEL TODAY:

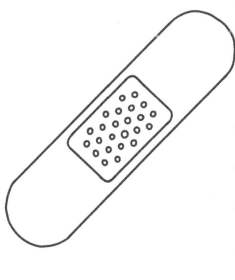

DATE: _____
TIME: _____

WHAT THEY SEE
VS.
WHAT THEY DON'T

HOW I FEEL TODAY:

I ☺
☹

LET ME BE
GREAT

WHAT PUSHES MY BUTTONS?

DATE: _____
TIME: _____

HOW I FEEL TODAY:

PUSH

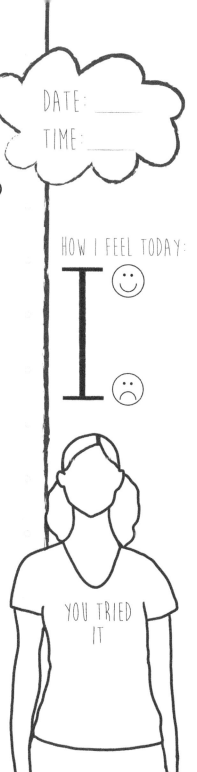

YOU TRIED IT

DATE: _____
TIME: _____

WISH UPON A ST★R.

HOW I FEEL TODAY: 😊 ☹️

DON'T STOP!

MY BALL OF EMOTIONS

DATE: _____
TIME: _____

HOW I FEEL TODAY:

#WINNING!

MAKING A BIG DEAL OUT OF NOTHING

DATE: _____
TIME: _____

HOW I FEEL TODAY:

MY LATEST OVERREACTION

WHERE'S MY CAPE?

DATE: _____
TIME: _____

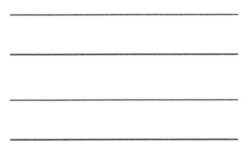

WORKING TO CHANGE THIS:

HOW I FEEL TODAY:

I

😊

☹️

_____

_____

_____

_____

IT TAKES A VILLAGE

CLIMBING

TOWARDS...

DATE: _____

TIME: _____

HOW I FEEL TODAY:

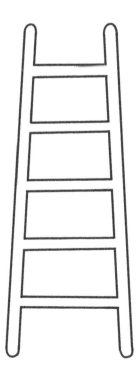

IT'S ABOVE
ME NOW

DATE: _____
TIME: _____

UNDECIDED ABOUT...

HOW I FEEL TODAY:

THIS IS ME

GIVING BACK BY...

DATE: _____
TIME: _____

HOW I FEEL TODAY:

I 🙂
  🙁

VOLUNTEER

OVERACHIEVER

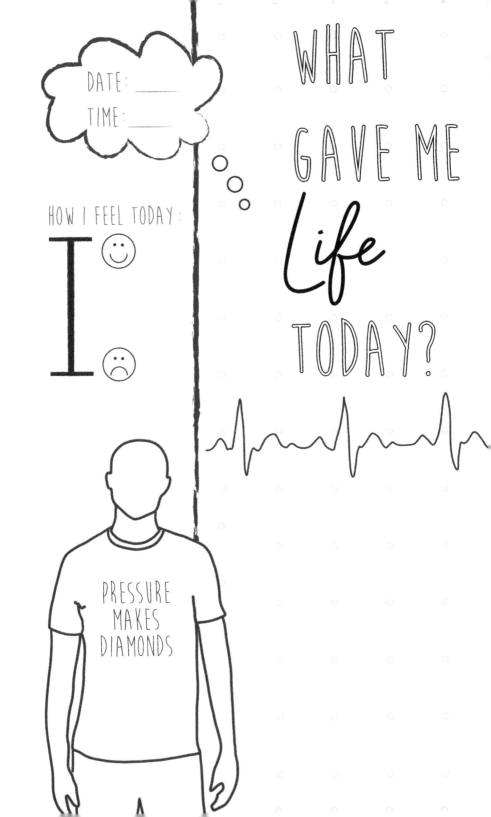

ANXIOUS ABOUT...

DATE: ______

TIME: ______

HOW I FEEL TODAY:

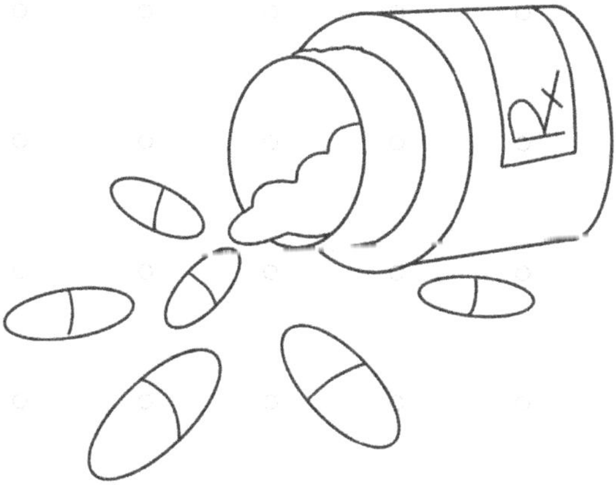

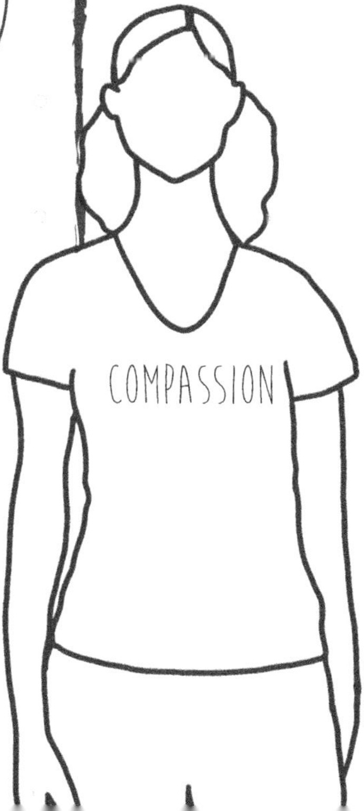

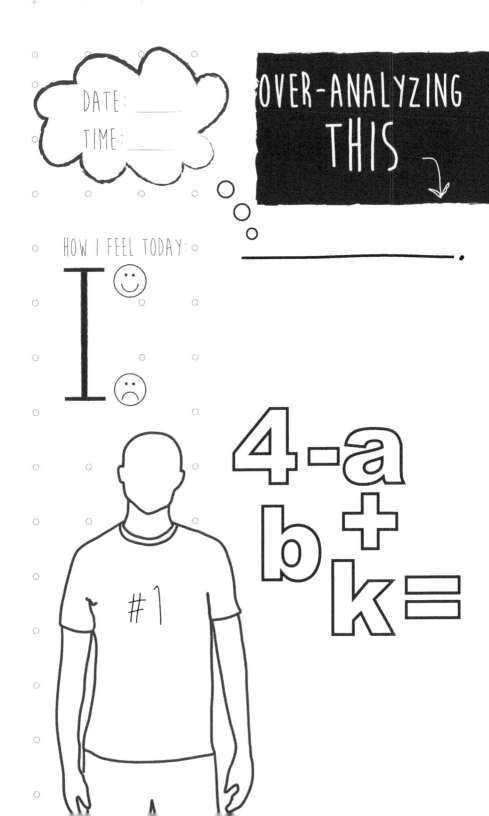

MY "AHA" MOMENT

DATE: _____
TIME: _____

HOW I FEEL TODAY:

CLASSIC

HOW DO I SOOTHE MY SOUL?

DATE: _____
TIME: _____

HOW I FEEL TODAY:

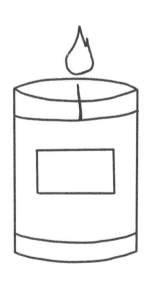

GOAL DIGGER

DATE: _____
TIME: _____

CLEANING HOUSE
(PEOPLE OR THINGS)

HOW I FEEL TODAY:

ROYALTY

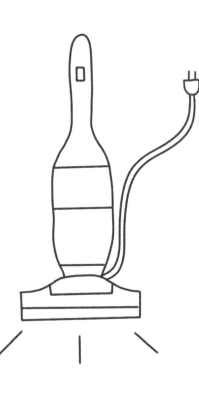

MY PROUDEST MOMENT

DATE: _____

TIME: _____

HOW I FEEL TODAY:

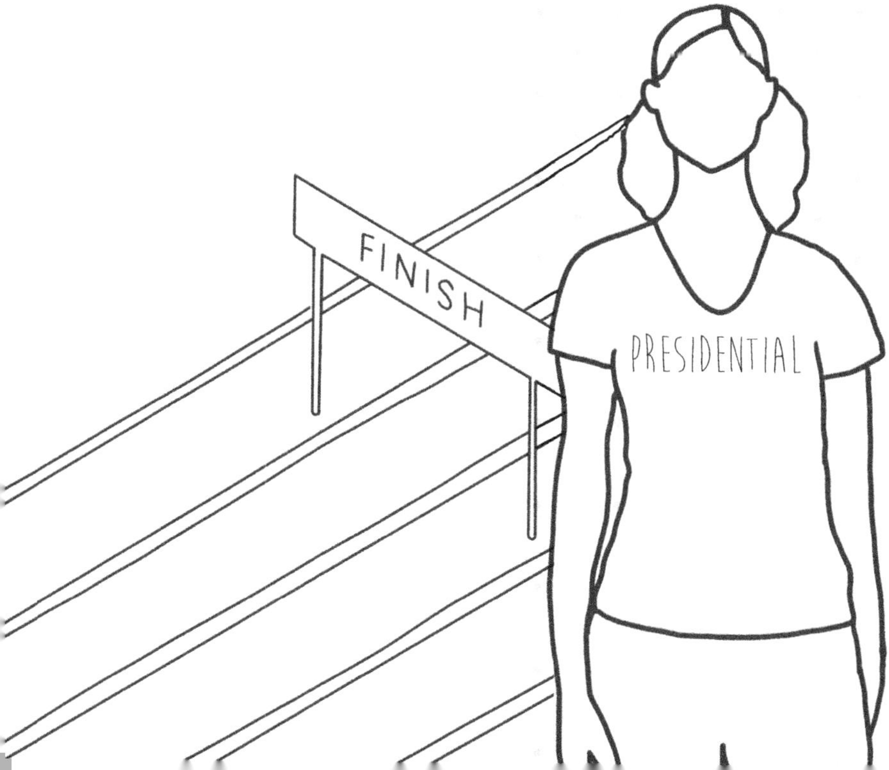

FINISH

PRESIDENTIAL

DATE: _____
TIME: _____

DOES MY VOTE COUNT?

HOW I FEEL TODAY:

VOTE

BLACK AND PROUD

WHAT PROVIDES ME SECURITY AND SAFETY?

DATE: _____
TIME: _____

HOW I FEEL TODAY:

AU NATURALE

THINGS THAT MAKE ME HAPPY

IT'S OKAY TO.....

CREATE YOUR OWN

MASTERPIECE

OUTSIDE
MY
CONTROL

INSIDE
MY
CONTROL

GUIDELINES FOR TRACKING YOUR MOOD:

1. In the blank squares on the mood tracker pages, assign a color to the emotion by coloring it in.

2. Identify the day of the month then color in the image that best describes your mood that day.

3. Once the page is complete, take note of your mental space and reflect on how these emotions have impacted you this month.

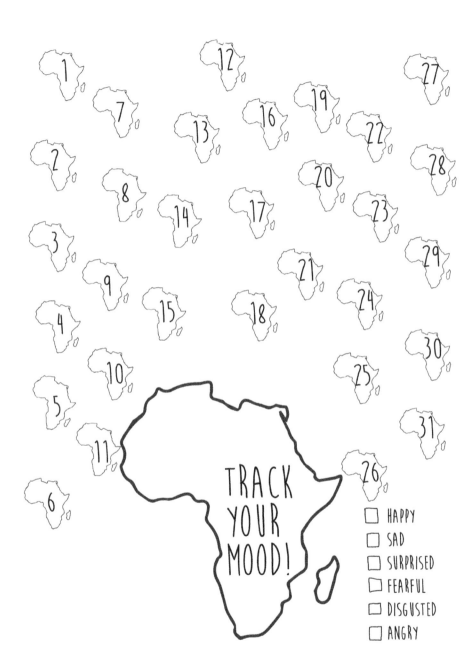

TRACK YOUR
MOOD!

- ☐ HAPPY
- ☐ SAD
- ☐ SURPRISED
- ☐ FEARFUL
- ☐ DISGUSTED
- ☐ ANGRY

TRACK YOUR MOOD!

☐ HAPPY
☐ SAD
☐ SURPRISED
☐ FEARFUL
☐ DISGUSTED
☐ ANGRY

YOU MADE IT!

Congratulations on making it to the end! This has been an eye-opening experience, right? Coloring, doodling, and/or sketching may reduce stress and symptoms of anxiety and depression while increasing mindfulness and relaxation. So, let's reflect.

What did you learn about yourself?
What unresolved emotions were you able
to identify?
What will you challenge yourself to do differently?
Moving forward, how will you practice self-care?

Now pat yourself on the back and most importantly, **TREAT YO SELF!**

Note: If you realize you need more support, seek help from a mental health professional. If you require immediate attention, call 9-1-1 or go to your nearest hospital.

Be Safe! Be Well! **Be YOU!**

Made in the USA
Las Vegas, NV
16 July 2021